EXTRAORDINARY ANIMALS

EXTRAORDINARY ANIMALS

Phillip and Teresa Coffey

For Louise and Emma

ARNOLD - WHEATON

Arnold-Wheaton
A Division of E. J. Arnold & Son Limited
Registered office at
Parkside Lane, Leeds LS11 5TD
and at
Hennock Road, Exeter EX2 8RP

A subsidiary of Pergamon Press Ltd
Headington Hill Hall, Oxford OX3 0BW

Pergamon Press Inc.
Maxwell House, Fairview Park, Elmsford, New York 10523

Pergamon Press Canada Ltd
Suite 104, 150 Consumers Road, Willowdale, Ontario M2J 1P9

Pergamon Press (Australia) Pty Ltd
P.O. Box 544, Potts Point, N.S.W. 2011

Pergamon Press GmbH
Hammerweg 6, D-6242 Kronberg, Federal Republic of Germany

First published 1985

ACKNOWLEDGEMENTS

The authors would like to thank the following individuals and zoos for allowing them to photograph their animals. Particular thanks go to the zoo-keepers, who in many cases allowed the authors behind barriers and off view areas to take photographs.

Basle Zoological Gardens (2, 15, 24, 38); Blackpool Zoological Gardens (30); Bristol Zoological Gardens (8, 16); Bryan Carrol (48); Cologne Zoological Gardens (1); Cotswold Wildlife Park (21); Frankfurt Zoological Gardens (14, 23, 31, 34, 42); Gharial Breeding Project, Royal Chitwan National Park, Nepal (32); Jersey Aquarium (45, 46); Jersey Wildlife Preservation Trust (3, 4, 6, 9, 20, 25, 26, 27, 33, 35, 39, 40, 49, 50); Marwell Zoological Society (7); North of England Zoological Society, Chester (12, 13, 17); Wildfowl Trust, Slimbridge (19); Wilhelma Zoological and Botanical Gardens, Stuttgart (10, 41, 47); H. Zimmerman (36, 43); Zoological Gardens, Regent's Park (5, 18, 44); Zurich Zoological Gardens (22, 28, 37).

The authors would also like to thank Jeremy Mallinson, Nick Lindsay, Quentin Bloxham, Simon Tonge, David Jeggo and Erica Bastiman for their help with the manuscript.

Printed in Great Britain by A. Wheaton & Co. Ltd, Hennock Road, Exeter

ISBN 0 08–029299–2

INTRODUCTION

An astonishing variety of animal life has evolved on earth since life began, 3200 million years ago. In this book you will find fifty extraordinary animals, ranging from the killer whale to the greenfly and including a fish that climbs trees, a marsupial with its own parachute and a lizard that can run over water.

Some animals have had to adapt to their environment in ingenious ways in order to survive. The African lungfish, for example, buries itself in a mud cocoon during periods of drought and can wait for as long as four years until the rains come. The musk ox has a shaggy coat to protect it from the harsh winters of its Arctic habitat, and soft pads on its feet so that it can walk on snow. The fennec fox, on the other hand, manages to survive in the scorching heat of the Sahara Desert, where water and food are extremely scarce.

Many animals have adapted to suit the type of food they eat. For example, the African spoonbill's curious-looking beak efficiently sifts tiny animals from the water, while the alligator snapping turtle uses its own tongue as bait to catch fish. The Tasmanian devil has tremendously powerful jaws and can crush bone; it devours every bit of its prey. The cheetah, which relies on speed to chase and bring down its prey, has become the fastest animal on land.

Colouring is used in different ways. Some animals are brightly coloured so that they can recognize or attract their own species. Others use clever camouflage to fade into the background; Jackson's chameleon and the Asiatic horned toad are very good examples of this. The harmless Sinaloan milk snake's colouring is a copy of a poisonous snake's markings, and the peacock butterfly's four "eyes" frighten would-be predators. The white tiger and the black jaguar are examples of the unusual colour variations that can crop up among normal-coloured animals.

Poison also has various uses. The western diamond-back rattlesnake uses it to kill, the red-kneed tarantula to paralyse its prey and the dragon fish for self-defence.

Some of the more bizarre features of various species in this book cannot be fully explained. The male mandrill's spectacular markings and the male Jackson's chameleon's three horns probably make them attractive to the females, but no one can really account for the male proboscis monkey's large nose, the red uakari's peculiar appearance or the tuatara's hidden extra eye.

At the end of the book you will find suggestions for finding out more about extraordinary animals, a book list and a glossary.

The following animals appear in this book:

1. red uakari
2. proboscis monkey
3. mandrill
4. sugar glider
5. Tasmanian devil
6. cheetah
7. jaguar
8. white tiger
9. fennec fox
10. elephant seal
11. killer whale
12. Ankole cattle
13. musk ox
14. babirusa
15. okapi
16. king penguin
17. ostrich
18. one-wattled cassowary
19. black swan
20. saddlebill stork
21. African spoonbill
22. scarlet ibis
23. Andean condor
24. red-thighed falconet
25. Victoria crowned pigeon
26. blue and yellow macaw
27. white-crested touraco
28. great grey owl
29. great Indian hornbill
30. Aldabra tortoise
31. alligator snapping turtle
32. gharial
33. tuatara
34. Jackson's chameleon
35. plumed basilisk
36. stump-tailed skink
37. gila monster
38. Komodo dragon
39. reticulated python
40. Sinaloan milk snake
41. western diamond-back rattlesnake
42. Asiatic horned frog
43. red-eyed tree-frog
44. African lungfish
45. red piranha
46. dragon fish
47. mudskipper
48. red-kneed tarantula
49. peacock butterfly
50. greenfly

1 red uakari

Cacajao calvus rubicundus

Distribution: eastern Peru and western Brazil
Habitat: tropical rain forest
Diet: fruit, berries, nuts, leaves and small animals, including bats

The red uakari gets its name not from the colour of its face but from the reddish-brown of its fur. When it is healthy, the uakari's face is a bright scarlet; its face looks bald, but has a sparse covering of short white hairs. Uakaris' long, coarse fur helps to protect them from the frequent downpours in their rain-forest home.

Living in groups numbering between ten and a hundred, these monkeys spend almost all their time in the tree-tops. They can move nimbly along the branches, on all fours, but cannot make large leaps from one tree to the next. For many months of the year the forest floor is flooded, making it very difficult for them to move about.

Female uakaris give birth to a single infant once every two years.

The red uakari has a shorter tail than any other South American monkey.

2 proboscis monkey

Nasalis larvatus

Distribution: Borneo
Habitat: forests, freshwater deltas and mangrove swamps
Diet: leaves, shoots and buds

The proboscis (pronounced probossis) monkey gets its name from the adult male's long, bulbous nose, which keeps growing throughout his life and may become as much as ten centimetres long. The male often has to push his nose out of the way when he is eating! His nose straightens out when he makes his loud, honking alarm calls. Female proboscis monkeys have a short, upturned nose.

Proboscis monkeys usually live in groups, moving about slowly as they feed. Because their food provides little nourishment, they have to eat a great deal to satisfy their needs. In waterlogged swamps they can jump or swim from tree to tree.

The young are born with sky-blue faces that turn grey when they are about three months old. They are very active and play together, often swinging on their parents' tails and teasing them by pulling their noses.

3 mandrill

Mandrillus sphinx

Distribution: Nigeria, Cameroun, Gabon, Congo, Zaire and Guinea
Habitat: forest
Diet: plants, fruit, roots and small animals such as insects, worms, mice, snakes and lizards

The male mandrill is one of the most colourful Primates, with sky-blue and red markings on his face and violet and scarlet on his rump. These strong colours show that he is a mature male. Female mandrills are about half the size of the males.

The male mandrill occasionally displays his dominance by yawning to show off his long canine teeth. He may also slap the ground with his hand and raise the hair on his shoulders. This frightening behaviour is usually enough to deal with any threats, and actual violence is not necessary. Another expression mandrills make, raising their lips to show their teeth, looks aggressive but is really a friendly gesture.

Mandrills live in troupes numbering from a few up to 50. They spend much of the day on the ground, searching for food, but at night they climb into trees to sleep in safety.

4 sugar glider

Petaurus breviceps

Distribution: Australia (including Tasmania) and Papua New Guinea
Habitat: forest
Diet: nectar, sap and flowers as well as insects and small animals

As its name implies, the sugar glider has a sweet tooth and can glide through the air.

On either side of the sugar glider's body, between its arms and legs, there is a fold of skin that acts like a parachute. When the sugar glider wants to move from one tree to another it simply jumps into the air and stretches out its arms and legs. It can glide for distances of 40 metres or more, steering with its bushy tail and by pulling its "parachute" folds of skin with its hind legs.

During the day groups of sugar gliders curl up in holes in trees lined with leaves, emerging at night to wander about the tree-tops in search of food. Their acute sense of smell helps them to find flowers rich in nectar.

The sugar glider is a marsupial; the females have a pouch for their young.

5 Tasmanian devil

Sarcophilus harrisii

Distribution: Tasmania
Habitat: forest
Diet: mammals such as wallabies and rat-kangaroos, birds, lizards and carrion

The Tasmanian devil was given its name by the early settlers of Tasmania. Apparently it is very aggressive when disturbed: it snaps and snarls and its pale-pink ears turn red!

A strong, cunning animal with teeth that can crush bone, the Tasmanian devil is not afraid to attack animals larger than itself. It holds down its prey with its front paws and devours it, skin, bones, fur and all. It sleeps during the day and is active at night.

The Tasmanian devil was once found in eastern Australia and used to be common in Tasmania, but the first settlers persecuted it as a chicken thief and it is now quite rare.

Like many Australian mammals, the Tasmanian devil is a marsupial. The female's pouch opens towards her tail rather than towards her head; Tasmanian devils burrow in the ground, so this arrangement prevents soil from getting into the pouch.

The female builds a nest in the ground, in a hollow log or in a cave and lines it with grass and leaves. She gives birth to her young after a short gestation period (about 31 days). At first she carries them in her pouch but when they are about a hundred days old she leaves them in the nest. The male Tasmanian devil seems to play no part in rearing the young.

6 jaguar

Panthera onca

Distribution: Central and South America
Habitat: forest, marsh, scrubland and grassland
Diet: tapirs, deer, birds, capybaras, boa constrictors and
    peccaries

The jaguar is the largest cat found in North or South America. Often mistaken for a leopard because of its spotted coat, it is larger than the leopard, has a broader head and its circular spots (called rosettes) often have a dot in the middle.

Like leopards, however, jaguars are sometimes black. Black jaguars are not a different species, as was once thought, but occur among normal-coloured jaguar populations. In fact it is possible for a female to have a litter of young that includes some black cubs and some yellow ones. Black jaguars are really dark brown rather than black, with the usual black spots.

Jaguars are solitary animals as a rule. They hunt animals such as tapirs and capybaras that are often found in water, so they need to be good swimmers. They get as close as they can to their prey, then pounce with great power and agility. They often drag small animals into a nearby tree to eat them.

7   white tiger

Panthera tigris

White tigers are not a separate species, but a colour variation of the Bengal tiger, which is yellow with black stripes. They are not true albinos because they do not have red eyes. Their eyes are blue and their skin is greyish-pink. They have white or creamy-white fur with pale-brown stripes.

It would be very unusual to find a white tiger living in the wild in India, but several were killed there in the first half of this century, when tiger-hunting was popular. Then, in 1951, a white tiger was captured in the State of Rewa (now part of Madhya Pradesh) in India. A female Bengal tiger and three of her cubs had been shot in a hunt. The fourth cub, which was white, was later captured and kept at the palace of the Maharajah of Rewa.

This tiger, named Mohan, was mated with a normal-coloured tigress. All their cubs were yellow. Then Mohan was mated with one of his daughters and her first litter consisted of four white cubs. This line of white tigers gave rise to all those known to be in captivity today.

8   cheetah

Acinonyx jubatus

Distribution: Africa and western Asia
Habitat: grassland and open woodland
Diet: medium-sized antelope, small mammals and birds

The fastest animal on land, the cheetah can reach speeds of just over 100 k.p.h., but only over distances of less than 500 metres. It is a solitary hunter and chases its prey rather than pouncing on it.

The cheetah's body is adapted for speed in these ways: its small head and slender body make it streamlined; its spine is supple and, with its long legs, gives it a very long stride; it has powerful leg and back muscles; its long tail helps it balance, and its claws grip the ground like running shoes. (The cheetah is the only member of the cat family that cannot retract – draw in – its claws. For this reason, its claws are blunt and are not used to grip prey as most cats do.)

Young cheetahs are often preyed upon by lions and hunting dogs. They are also sensitive to the presence of people. Consequently, cheetahs are now rare and found in any numbers only in some game parks in Namibia.

9 fennec fox

Fennecus zerda

Distribution: North Africa, Sinai peninsula and Arabia
Habitat: desert and semi-desert
Diet: insects, lizards and rodents

The fennec fox is the smallest member of the fox family, being only 38 centimetres long, including its tail. Its huge ears can be up to ten centimetres long.

The desert is one of the harshest of habitats. During the day fennec foxes stay in their underground burrows, to keep cool. There may be as many as ten foxes living together and they usually dig several dens that interconnect. The hairs on the pads of their feet protect them from the scorching sand if they do have to come out in the day.

At night the foxes come out to search for food, which is so scarce that they will try to catch almost anything. With their large eyes and enormous ears, they have excellent senses of sight and hearing.

In the desert there may be no rain for several years, but the fennec fox can survive for long periods without drinking any water. It gets the liquid it needs from its food.

10 elephant seal

Mirounga leonina

Distribution: sub-Antarctic islands, the coast of southern Argentina and the open sea
Habitat: the sea (except during the breeding season)
Diet: fish and cuttlefish

The elephant seal is the largest member of the seal family. Fully grown bulls can weigh 3700 kilos and measure up to six metres in length. In contrast, females weigh only 900 kilos.

At the beginning of their two-month breeding season elephant seals come ashore on deserted islands. The males fight fiercely among themselves, sometimes inflicting serious injuries. The adult male's trunk (which gave the species its name) becomes more obvious during the breeding season, when it swells and hangs over the seal's mouth. The dominant bull guards his area of the beach and gathers a harem of cows. Having mated the previous season, the cows (females) give birth to a single pup shortly after coming on to land.

When elephant seals moult, their fur comes off in large patches, together with the outer layers of skin. New, sleek fur grows in its place.

11 killer whale

Orcinus orca

Distribution: worldwide
Habitat: cold seas
Diet: other whales, seals, penguins, fish and squid

The killer whale, or orca, has the reputation of being a ruthless predator. Killer whales hunt in packs of up to 40, and work efficiently together as they chase and attack their prey. They have about 50 sharp, pointed teeth, those of the upper and lower jaws interlocking with each other.

Killer whales have been known to play with food by tossing it into the air before tearing it apart with their teeth. They may also lift themselves on to the ice to knock seals into the water and eat them. Their only real enemy is man.

The killer whale's black-and-white markings are good camouflage. It has a tall dorsal fin that can sometimes be seen above the water; in some males this fin may be nearly two metres high. The largest member of the dolphin and porpoise family, the killer whale may weigh as much as 8000 kilos. The average length of an adult is eight metres.

The females give birth to a single calf after a gestation period of between twelve and fourteen months. Whales are mammals, so the calf is fed on its mother's milk at first.

12 Ankole cattle

Bos indicus

Distribution: East Africa, particularly Uganda
Diet: grass

Ankole cattle are domesticated animals. Their ancestors are thought to have been long-horned wild oxen from the Nile Valley, first domesticated between 6000 and 4000 B.C.

There are several varieties of Ankole cattle, usually named after the tribes they belong to. Owning a large number is regarded as a sign of wealth. These animals are important in tribal ceremonies and are sometimes ritually slaughtered. Some tribes bleed them and use the blood as part of their diet, while in some areas they are used for pulling loads and for ploughing.

Ankole cattle may be deep red, red and white, black, black and white or greyish white. Strangely enough, the females have longer horns than the males.

13 musk ox

Ovibos moschatus

Distribution: northern Canada, Alaska, Greenland, Norway and the U.S.S.R.
Habitat: tundra
Diet: lichen, moss and coarse grass

The musk ox's warm coat helps it to withstand the harsh winters of its Arctic habitat, where the whole herd will often huddle together for warmth. The coat is made up of a short inner layer with an outer layer of long hair called guard hair that reaches almost to the ground. In the summer the ox moults and its coat is much shorter.

In winter, when food is very scarce, musk oxen scrape away the snow with their hard-rimmed hooves to find lichen and moss. Their hooves are curved and have soft pads that enable them to walk on snow.

Herds of these oxen are sometimes attacked by wolves. When this happens the adults form a tight circle with the calves in the middle. Both the males and the females lower their heads and use their horns as weapons to defend the herd.

In the spring the females give birth to a single calf after a gestation period of about eight months. Soon after it is born the calf can stand and keep up with the herd as it moves from place to place in a constant search for food.

14 babirusa

Babyrousa babyrussa

Distribution: Sulawesi and nearby islands
Habitat: swampy forest and the shores of rivers and lakes
Diet: leaves and fruit

The Indonesians called this animal *babirusa* ("pig deer") because they thought the male's tusks looked like a deer's antlers.

A distant relative of the pig, the babirusa has most unusual tusks. Instead of curving down outside the jaws, the upper tusks turn upwards, through the muzzle, and then curve backwards. (The Indonesians believe that the babirusa hooks its tusks over a branch at night and sleeps hanging in the air!) The upper tusks are probably used to defend the animal when it fights, while the lower ones are used as weapons of attack; the babirusa scrapes them against tree trunks to sharpen them.

The babirusa's crumpled skin looks hairless but is in fact sparsely covered with short, whitish-grey hairs.

Always alert to danger, this animal has very keen senses of smell and hearing and can run quickly. It is also a good swimmer, and likes to wallow in mud.

Babirusa live in small groups and the females give birth to two young after a gestation period of four or five months.

15 okapi

Okapia johnstoni

Distribution: Zaire
Habitat: equatorial forest
Diet: leaves, buds, fruit and seeds

The okapi is a close relative of the giraffe. Its preferred habitat is dense equatorial forest and because it is so secretive it was not discovered until 1900.

Its short, chocolate-coloured coat is sleek, like plush velvet, and the creamy-white stripes on its rump help to camouflage it in the dark forest. Male okapis have two small horns that continue to grow throughout their life. The horns are covered with skin and hair.

The okapi has a very long tongue that it uses to strip leaves from high branches and to clean its whole body, including its ears and eyes. Hearing is its best-developed sense and it can move its large ears to point forwards or backwards.

The okapi is sometimes solitary, but may also live in small family groups. A single calf is born after a gestation period of about fourteen and a half months. It is very similar in appearance to the adults.

16 king penguin

Aptenodytes patagonica

Distribution: Antarctic and sub-Antarctic islands
Habitat: the sea; barren and rocky islands for nesting
Diet: plankton, fish and squid

There are eighteen different species of penguin. The king penguin is the second largest, weighing between fifteen and 21 kilos and growing to a height of about 80 centimetres.

Adult king penguins spend much of their time at sea, swimming and catching their food. These birds are perfectly adapted to life in the water.

In the early spring the breeding adults return to land, where they form colonies numbering several thousand pairs. The parents take turns to incubate the single egg laid by the female, keeping it on top of their feet next to a fold of skin called the brood patch.

The chicks do not have time to develop before the onset of winter, so they stay on land in large groups, or crèches. Their parents return from time to time to feed them. However, many chicks fall prey to marauding giant petrels and some may be caught and eaten by leopard seals. The remaining chicks mature the following season.

In the past, thousands of king penguins were killed and their bodies boiled to extract oil.

17 ostrich

Struthio camelus

Distribution: Africa
Habitat: grassland, savannah
Diet: plant material including leaves, shoots, fruit and seeds; insects, rodents and small reptiles

The ostrich is the largest living bird, so big that it cannot fly. Adult males may be as much as two and a half metres tall and weigh up to 160 kilos – about twice the weight of a man. If attacked, an ostrich may fight back fiercely, using the two huge claws on each foot as weapons, or run swiftly away. Ostriches can reach speeds of up to 60 k.p.h., with long strides covering four and a half metres.

The male ostrich has black and white feathers on his wings and tail but the female is a dull grey-brown. In the breeding season, they perform an elaborate courtship display and then the male selects a nest-site.

Here the female lays her eggs. Each egg is about eighteen centimetres long and weighs about one and a half kilos – the equivalent of about 30 hen's eggs! The female keeps the eggs in the shade and fans them with her wings from time to time to protect them from the hot African sun. The male also helps to incubate the eggs. Large numbers of young ostriches sometimes band together in a crèche (nursery) guarded by a few adult birds.

Ostriches have excellent eyesight; their eyes are larger than those of any other bird.

18 one-wattled cassowary

Casuarius unappendiculatus

Distribution: Papua New Guinea
Habitat: dense forest, on flat ground
Diet: fallen fruit

The one-wattled cassowary is second only to the ostrich in size. Like the ostrich and a near relative, the emu, it cannot fly. If disturbed, it dashes through the undergrowth, along paths and tunnels, with its head stretched forwards. The horny lump on its head (called a casque or helmet) is thought to brush aside overhanging vegetation.

Apart from some short bristles, the cassowary has no feathers on its head or neck. Its legs are sturdy and end in three toes. The inner toe of each foot has a claw ten centimetres long that grips the ground when the bird is running. The claw is also a formidable weapon of defence.

The cassowary normally lives on its own and because of its shy nature is not often seen. The male and female stay together for the breeding season, finding each other by making a loud, low-pitched honking noise. The female lays between three and eight green eggs in a nest lined with leaves and grass. Only the male incubates the eggs, which takes about 52 days. On hatching, the chicks are a light brown colour with darker stripes.

19 black swan

Cygnus atratus

Distribution: Australia (including Tasmania) and New Zealand
Habitat: shallow freshwater and brackish lakes
Diet: water-weeds and other vegetation

It is quite common to see black swans in Australia and most people like them. Unfortunately, some fishermen claim that swans reduce the numbers of fish by eating the plants fish feed on, and farmers also complain when large flocks of several thousand swans feed on their cereal crops.

Generally, however, black swans feed on water plants. It was for this reason that some were introduced into New Zealand in the early 1860s, in the hope that they would clear rivers of clogging weed. Some were also introduced as game birds for hunting and for their ornamental value. Now the numbers of black swans have risen so dramatically in New Zealand that they are regarded as pests.

Like most swans, black swans mate for life. They build nests on islands in the middle of lakes, or on rafts of floating vegetation. When the cygnets hatch one of the parents may carry them on its back for the first few days.

When they migrate black swans fly in a line or in a V-shaped formation.

20 saddlebill stork

Ephippiorhynchus senegalensis

Distribution: Africa from Ethiopia to South Africa
Habitat: lakes, rivers, swamps and marshes
Diet: insects, fish, frogs, birds and small mammals

The saddlebill stork gets its name from the yellow plate near the top of its beak, which looks like a smooth leather saddle.

The saddlebill stork wades slowly and deliberately in shallow water looking for small animals. It has large eyes and excellent eyesight. When it spots an animal, the stork lunges at it with lightning speed and catches it with its long, sword-shaped beak. The prey probably dies instantly. The stork tosses the carcass into the air several times before crushing it in its beak. It swallows the limp morsel whole.

At the beginning of the breeding season the male and female carry out a ritual courtship dance. They then select a nest-site, usually on a flat-topped tree or bush, and build a large nest of twigs and small branches. The female lays two or three white eggs which are incubated for about 34 days. To begin with, the young are a mottled blackish-brown and white with a brown beak.

21 African spoonbill

Platalea alba

Distribution: Africa south of the Sahara
Habitat: shallow lakes, swamps and marshes
Diet: water insects and small animals

African spoonbills usually live in small flocks that gather with other birds such as storks, ibis and herons. As they wade about in shallow water stirring up the mud in search of food, they move their curiously shaped beak from side to side, keeping it pointing straight down. They trap and swallow water shrimps and other small creatures and let the water drain out through "sieves" along the edges of their beak.

At the beginning of the breeding season there is much excitement in the spoonbill colony: the birds build nests and perform courtship displays involving dancing and head-bowing. Each pair of spoonbills makes a flat platform of twigs, usually in the branches of a tree overhanging water, and lines it with dried reeds. Here the female lays three or four eggs. Both parents incubate the eggs.

When a parent feeds it, the chick eagerly pushes its beak into the adult's mouth to get the regurgitated food. A spoonbill chick's beak is quite short and flat at first but later on it grows longer and the tip becomes spoon-shaped.

22 scarlet ibis

Eudocimus ruber

Distribution: Trinidad and occasionally in Venezuela, Guyana, Surinam, French Guiana and Brazil
Habitat: mangrove swamps
Diet: worms and crustaceans such as small crabs

The scarlet ibis is entirely scarlet except for some of its wing feathers, which are tipped with black. The rich colouring is caused by a pigment called carotene (because it is found in carrots) in the bird's food. Without carotene, the ibis's feathers would be pale pink. Scarlet ibis were once common, but large numbers of them have been killed for their feathers and for food.

During the breeding season the birds pair and build nests in the branches of mangrove trees. Several hundred birds may nest in a small area. The male searches for twigs and brings them to the female, who uses them to build a frail nest. She lays two or three eggs and she and the male take turns to sit on them. The chicks hatch after about 22 days and are fed on partly digested food by both parents.

The scarlet ibis probes about in soft mud with its long, thin, down-curving beak in search of food.

23 Andean condor

Vultur gryphus

Distribution: the whole western side of South America
Habitat: open country in the high Andes and on the Pacific coast
Diet: carrion, including dead whales, llamas, cattle, sheep and many smaller animals

The Andean condor is one of the largest birds in the world, with a wing span of three metres. With its long, broad wings it soars effortlessly, high in the sky, and searches for food. Its sharp eyes can spot the body of a dead animal from a height of about 6000 metres.

The condor holds down the carcass with its sturdy feet, then tears off pieces of flesh with its powerful hooked beak. Food can be quite scarce, so when the condor has a chance to eat its fill it may eat so much that for a while it is unable to fly.

Andean condors nest on remote mountain ledges and lay only one egg. The incubation period is long (about 55 days) and the chick grows slowly. It will be six years old before it can breed.

Because its size, the Andean condor was worshipped by the Incas and now appears on the coat of arms of several South America countries.

24 red-thighed falconet

Microhierax caerulescens

Distribution: northern India, Burma and Indo-China
Habitat: open wooded areas
Diet: insects and small birds

The red-thighed falconet is probably the smallest bird of prey in the world, being only about the size of a sparrow.

During the day a pair of falconets usually sit on a tree branch, darting out quickly to catch insects such as dragonflies and butterflies. If a swarm of insects appears, the birds fly around in circles, eating them on the wing.

The falconet normally carries its prey back to its perch to eat it, but when it kills larger prey on the ground it may eat it there. The red-thighed falconet sometimes attacks birds larger than itself and in India has been trained by falconers to hunt larks and quail.

At night a pair of falconets may roost in the hollow of a rotten tree. They seem to prefer holes dug out by other birds, such as woodpeckers. They lay their eggs where they roost, laying three or four white eggs at a time. Red-thighed falconets that nest in the Himalayas migrate further south for the winter.

25 Victoria crowned pigeon

Goura victoria

Distribution: northern Papua New Guinea
Habitat: forest
Diet: fruit and seeds

The Victoria crowned pigeon is the largest member of the pigeon family. It is a shy, rather heavily built bird that spends much of its time on the ground, hiding among the plants on the forest floor. If there is any hint of danger it will run along the ground instead of flying away. However, at night it flies to the top of a tree to roost in safety.

The feathers on the pigeon's head are lacy, open and fringed with white and make it look very graceful. The shape and colour of the crest help the bird to identify others of its own species.

During its courtship display, the male crowned pigeon bobs its head up and down. At the same time it makes a booming noise deep in its throat. The female nests in a compact nest of twigs five to seven metres up in a tree. She lays a single white egg, which the male helps her to incubate. This takes 30 days, and when the chick hatches both parents help to feed it on crop milk.

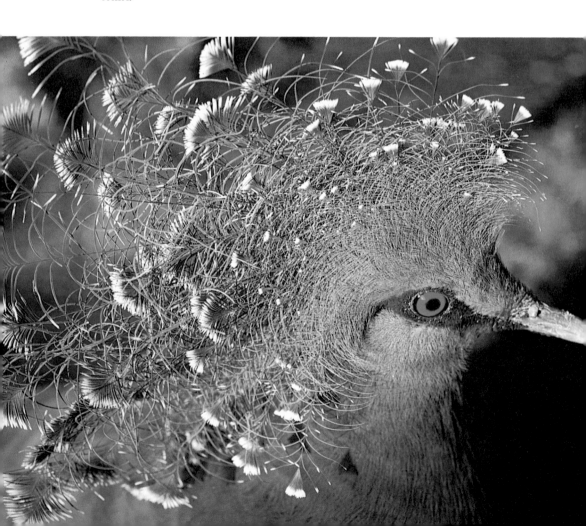

26 blue and yellow macaw

Ara ararauna

Distribution: South America
Habitat: tropical forest
Diet: fruit, nuts, flowers and leaves

These macaws pair for life, but out of the breeding season they fly around in flocks of several hundred birds. They roost in the same place each night, flying off above the forest canopy in the morning to look for food. If there is any danger, they leave their perches and fly into the air, screeching loudly to warn the others.

With its large, powerful beak the blue and yellow macaw can crack open the hard shells of nuts like Brazil nuts to reach the soft kernel inside. It also uses its beak to preen its feathers, to grip with as it moves along branches and to tear off pieces of soft fruit, which it holds in its claws.

The female lays two white eggs in a hole high up in a tree and incubates them for about 25 days. When the chicks are six months old it is difficult to distinguish them from the adults.

Like other macaws and parrots, blue and yellow macaws can imitate human speech, although they probably don't understand what they are saying!

27 white-crested touraco

Tauraco leucolophus

Distribution: Central Africa
Habitat: open forest and scrub
Diet: fruit

Touracos' colouring is caused by special pigments that no other birds have: their greeny-blue wings, which camouflage them amongst the forest trees, are coloured by a pigment called turacoverdin, and the crimson feathers of their underwings are coloured by a pigment called turacin.

The white-crested touracos' red underwings are usually glimpsed only briefly, when they dart from tree to tree, but during courtship displays the cock bird spreads his wings to show them off. Strangely enough, he may use the same display to threaten other birds.

White-crested touracos live in pairs and both the male and the female help to rear the young.

Touracos are distantly related to cuckoos.

28 great grey owl

Strix nebulosa

Distribution: northern Europe, North America and Asia
Habitat: coniferous forests
Diet: voles and shrews

The great grey owl is one of the largest owls. It has a thick covering of feathers to keep it warm, and this makes it seem even larger.

This owl is most active during the morning and evening. It hunts in open country, locating its prey with its acute sense of hearing. It sits on a perch, listening for voles or shrews, then swoops down silently and grasps the prey with its talons. The great grey owl eats only voles and shrews and will migrate outside its normal range to find a suitable supply of them.

In the breeding season, early in the year, a pair of owls will occupy a territory. They let others know by making a series of low, hooting noises, *hoo-hoo-hoo*. Instead of building their own nests, great grey owls use those abandoned by eagles or buzzards. When there are young owlets, the parent birds will attack any other animal that comes near.

29 great Indian hornbill

Buceros bicornis

Distribution: India and South-East Asia
Habitat: forest
Diet: fruit

The great Indian hornbill is one of the largest members of the hornbill family. Its huge, down-curved yellow beak, with the horny casque on top, is not as heavy as it looks, because it contains a number of air spaces.

The hornbill uses its beak to bite off fruit hanging at the ends of thin branches. It seems to toss the fruit in the air before catching it in its mouth and eating it.

A pair of great Indian hornbills usually stay together for life and may use the same nest-site each breeding season. When it is time to build a nest, the female goes into a hollow high up in a tree trunk. The male carries up mud and together they block up the entrance, with the female inside, sometimes adding bits of food, dung and so on to the mud to build the wall. They leave a slit or hole just big enough for the male to pass food through to the female and chicks.

The female remains walled in to incubate her eggs and rear the young, which takes three and a half to four months. During this time the male has to feed the family by himself, catching insects for the young to eat. When the young are ready to leave the nest they chip away to enlarge the hole in the wall. When all the chicks have left the nest the adults break down the wall.

30 Aldabra tortoise

Geochelone gigantea

Distribution: Aldabra Islands and the Seychelles (north of Madagascar)
Habitat: thick scrub
Diet: plants such as dried grass and leaves, and meat when available

The Aldabra tortoise is the largest land tortoise in the world and can reach a weight of 200 kilos. The males are usually larger than the females. Both have thick, muscular, pillar-shaped legs to support their massive bodies and are extremely slow-moving animals. At top speed (370 metres an hour) it would take them about fifteen minutes to walk the length of a football pitch.

Aldabra tortoises feed in the early morning. By about nine o'clock the sun is too hot and they are forced to move into the shade or into water, and may spend much of the day wallowing in mud to keep cool. These tortoises are shy in the wild and will make a loud hissing noise and withdraw into their shell if approached.

In the breeding season (January to April) the females lay between nine and 25 eggs in the ground. The incubation period is 120 to 130 days.

Aldabra tortoises take between 20 and 25 years to mature and are thought to live for more than 150 years.

31 alligator snapping turtle

Macroclemmys temminckii

Distribution: in the Mississippi delta and between the Rocky Mountains and the Appalachians
Habitat: rivers and lakes
Diet: fish and other water animals

The alligator snapping turtle is the largest freshwater turtle in the world, weighing as much as 100 kilos and growing to a length of up to 75 centimetres.

The green algae that often grow on the turtle's knobbly shell camouflage it in murky water. This is an advantage to the turtle, which has a very peculiar way of getting its food: it is an angler!

The tip of the alligator snapping turtle's tongue is pink and forked and looks just like a worm. The turtle waits with its mouth wide open and twitches its tongue. Thinking they have spotted a tasty morsel of food, fish swim closer to investigate, and then – snap! – the turtle closes its powerful, hooked jaws and swallows the fish.

Adult turtles spend all their time in water, but the female must come on to land to lay her eggs, so that the young do not drown. She chooses a nest-site that will not become waterlogged, digs a hole and lays her eggs. When she has covered them with soil she returns to the water. When the young hatch, several months later, they too make for the river.

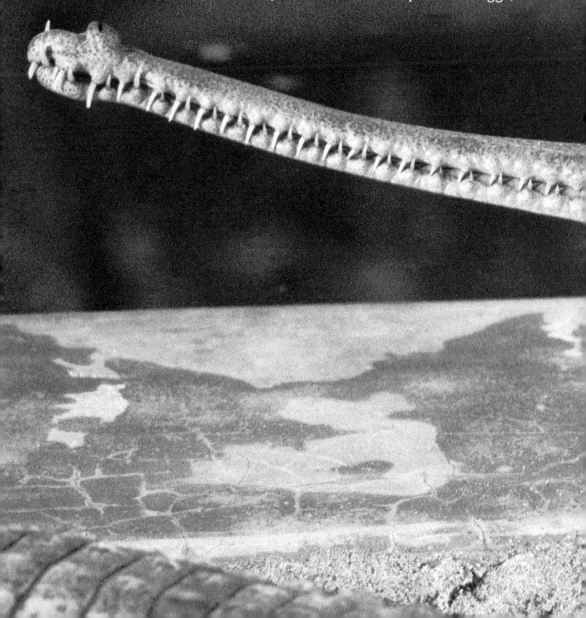

32 gharial

Gavialis gangeticus

Distribution: India and Nepal
Habitat: sandy banks of the Brahmaputra, Ganges and Mohanadi Rivers
Diet: mainly fish, but also frogs and other small animals

The gharial (or gavial) is well adapted to life in water. It has a long, flat tail and webbed hind feet to help push itself through the water and its long snout and sharp, outward-pointing teeth are ideal weapons for catching fish.

Gharials reach sexual maturity when they are about eight years old. At the beginning of the breeding season (January and February), large males stake out a territory and gather a harem of females. Two or three months later each female buries between 16 and 60 eggs in raised sandbanks. Traditionally, they would stay near the nest-site to protect the eggs, but this is no longer possible, because of human disturbance, so otters, monitor lizards and people are able to steal the eggs. The incubation period is about 80 days and the hatchlings are about 30 centimetres long.

The gharial is now endangered, with a wild population of about 200. In the Royal Chitwan Park in Nepal eggs from wild nests are taken away and incubated, and the young are then reared in safe enclosures. They are released back into the wild when they are about three years old, when they are no longer vulnerable to predators.

33 tuatara

Sphenodon punctatus

Distribution: some islands off the shores of New Zealand
Habitat: wooded slopes
Diet: insects, spiders, earthworms, snails and birds' eggs

This unique reptile is often called a living fossil, because it has remained unchanged for 200 million years – since before the time of the dinosaurs. Its name is a Maori word meaning "spinyback" (referring to the crest of scales down its back). It is sometimes described as "the lizard with three eyes", too. Its third eye, hidden beneath the skin on its head, is very similar in structure to a normal eye, but no one knows exactly what it is for.

The tuatara prefers a cool climate with a temperature of about 12°C. It finds these conditions on the wooded slopes of the islands where it lives, making its home in a burrow.

A very slow-growing animal, the tuatara takes about 20 years to become sexually mature and its eggs take up to fifteen months to incubate, longer than any other reptile eggs.

34 Jackson's chameleon

Chamaeleo jacksonii

Distribution: Tanzania and Kenya
Habitat: highland forest
Diet: insects such as grasshoppers, flies, butterflies and beetles

Male Jackson's chameleons have three horns on their snout made of skin (not bone) and covered with scales. Females have only the middle horn, with a small bump on either side.

These chameleons are adapted to living in trees. Their toes are arranged like pincers, to give a strong grip, and they have a prehensile tail. Their green colouring helps to camouflage them among the leaves and they can also make themselves a lighter or darker shade to match the colour of their surroundings more precisely. Chameleons can flatten themselves sideways, too, so that they are harder to see from the front.

Their eyes are on "turrets" that can move in all directions, independently of each other, making it easy for them to look around for food. When a chameleon spots an insect it focuses both eyes on it, shoots out its tongue and flicks the insect into its mouth. Unfolded, a chameleon's tongue is as long as its body; the tip is sticky, for catching insects.

Chameleons lick the dew on leaves to get water.

35 plumed basilisk

Basiliscus plumifrons

Distribution: Costa Rica
Habitat: tropical forest
Diet: insects, fruit, small birds and animals, including other
    species of lizard

This lizard was named after the mythical basilisk whose stare was said to turn people to stone. Its bright orange eyes, which flicker rapidly over its surroundings, do have a piercing gaze.

When it is sitting still in the forest trees the basilisk is perfectly camouflaged. It seems to prefer to sit on branches that overhang water and if, despite its camouflage, an attacker comes too close, it will jump into the water to escape. A good swimmer, it can also stay underwater, standing on the bottom, for several minutes. It is sometimes known as the "Jesus Christ lizard" because it can run on the surface of the water, rising up on its hind legs.

Only the male has the "plume" or crest on its head, back and tail.

36 stump-tailed skink

Tiliqua rugosa (Trachydosaurus rugosus)

Distribution: southern Australia
Habitat: sand dunes and other dry areas
Diet: leaves, fruit, insects, earthworms and snails

The stump-tailed skink is one of the strangest-looking lizards in Australia. Its short, fat tail looks the same shape as its head. Some people suggest that this is a device to confuse predators by making it hard for them to tell which way the skink is going. Others argue that its tail is just a useful place to store fat until it is needed. Certainly, after a long drought the tail gets much thinner.

This lizard reacts very oddly when threatened by predators: it rolls over and arches its back, hissing loudly. At the same time it opens its jaws wide to display its sky-blue tongue and bright-red mouth. As a last resort, the skink will bite.

The female gives birth to two or three live young. They are quite large, about half her size, which gives them a good start in life. They have to feed well before hibernating for the winter.

"Bobtail", "shingle-back" and "pine-cone lizard" are local names for this scaly-skinned animal.

37 gila monster

Heloderma suspectum

Distribution: south-western U.S.A. and north-western Mexico
Habitat: desert and semi-desert
Diet: nestling rodents and birds, and birds' and reptiles' eggs

The gila (pronounced heelah) monster is closely related to the only other poisonous lizard in the world, the beaded lizard. A slow-moving but powerful animal, it has strong jaws for holding on to prey while it injects poison. The poison is produced in a pair of special glands on either side of the back of the monster's lower jaw and travels along a groove in its back teeth.

A bite from a gila monster is not usually fatal to a human being, but it can cause shock, fainting, vomiting, loss of blood pressure, swelling around the wound and severe pain.

This lizard manages to survive in the desert by living off the fat stored in its tail. It can also survive drought, though it may become very thin.

The gila monster's distinctive pink and black blotches warn larger animals that it is poisonous.

38 Komodo dragon

Varanus komodoensis

Distribution: several Indonesian islands east of Java, including Komodo Island
Habitat: woodland and scrub
Diet: carrion and animals from insects to buffalo

The Komodo dragon is the largest living lizard, growing to a length of just over three metres. It uses its long, powerful claws and curved, jagged teeth to rip and tear its prey. Large dragons have been known to bring down big water buffalo, but their usual prey includes pigs and deer. They can devour an 18-kilo carcass in ten minutes!

Komodo dragons are useful animals because they eat carrion, which helps to prevent the spread of disease. They are often blamed when people mysteriously disappear and presumably die: their bite can produce a severe septic wound that causes death within a few days.

The females dig a hole in a sandy river bank and lay up to 30 soft, leather-shelled eggs. The incubation period is about eight months. When they hatch, the young dragons are half a metre long. At this stage they feed on insects but later on they will eat birds' eggs and whatever they can scavenge until they are large enough to kill for themselves. They mature when they are about six years old.

39 reticulated python

Python reticulatus

Distribution: South-East Asia
Habitat: tropical forest and scrub, including places near human dwellings
Diet: mammals and birds

The reticulated python is one of the largest snakes, sometimes reaching ten metres in length.

Like all snakes, this python lacks eyelids and ears. It is short-sighted, deaf and the only sound it makes is a loud hiss if threatened. In spite of these apparent disabilities, the reticulated python is very alert. It has an excellent sense of smell, using the tongue to take scent particles into its mouth, and it has an extra sense that we do not have. Along the edge of its upper jaw there are a number of pits that are sensitive to temperature and can detect the heat of warm-blooded prey.

The reticulated python kills its prey by constriction (squeezing the animal to death in its coils) and swallows it whole. Snakes are cold-blooded, so they do not need frequent meals. One reticulated python in Frankfurt Zoo went for one and a half years between meals!

The reticulated python is one of the few reptiles that shows any parental care. When the female lays her eggs, she coils around them to protect them. The incubation period is two to three months.

40 Sinaloan milk snake

Lampropeltis triangulum sinaloae

Distribution: Mexico
Habitat: desert and semi-desert areas
Diet: small rodents, birds, lizards and snakes, including poisonous ones

This snake is called a milk snake because it was mistakenly believed to steal vast quantities of milk from cows. (Sinaloa is a Mexican state.)

The Sinaloan milk snake's vivid red, yellow and black markings are a close copy of those of the coral snake, a snake that lives in the same area. This protects the milk snake from predators because, although it is not poisonous, the coral snake is, and the bright colouring is a warning to would-be attackers.

A secretive animal, the milk snake spends much of the day hiding under rocks. It is most active at night, when it comes out to search for prey, including small rattlesnakes. Rattlesnakes are helpless if attacked by the milk snake, which is not affected by their poison.

Milk snakes kill their prey by constriction (squeezing).

41 western diamond-back rattlesnake

Crotalus atrox

Distribution: south-western U.S.A. and northern Mexico
Habitat: scrub, desert and other dry areas
Diet: rodents and birds

The western diamond-back rattlesnake is one of the most dangerous, though not the largest, of the rattlesnakes. It can be aggressive if disturbed and probably causes more human deaths than any other snake in North America.

The rattlesnake injects poison into its victim through its hollow fangs. This affects the person's bloodstream, causes loss of blood pressure and internal bleeding and finally stops the heart.

Rattlesnakes use poison mainly to kill their prey, not people, however. They usually make a sort of sizzling sound with their rattle to warn larger animals, such as humans, cattle and horses, to keep away. The rattle is made up of several thin, horny, hollow segments at the end of the snake's tail. A new segment is added each time the snake sheds its skin.

When not in use, the rattlesnake's fangs are folded inside its mouth.

Rattlesnakes have a pit on either side of the face that detects the heat given off by warm-blooded prey. These pits are extremely accurate up to a distance of 50 centimetres.

Mating takes place in the spring and the female gives birth to about fifteen young five and a half months later. At first the young do not have a rattle, although they do have poison.

42 Asiatic horned frog

Megophrys monticola nasuta

Distribution: South-East Asia
Habitat: tropical forest
Diet: insects, worms, snails and small vertebrates such as other frogs and lizards

The Asiatic horned frog's "horns" are pointed flaps of skin above its eyes and nose.

This frog's markings (light brown with patches of darker brown) make it very hard to see among dead leaves on the forest floor. Small animals that do not notice it in time quickly disappear into its large mouth.

The Asiatic horned frog can produce a poisonous slime on its back to discourage predators.

During the breeding season the male croaks to attact a female. She lays thousands of jelly-coated eggs in strings, wrapping them round the stalks of water plants. The tadpoles soon hatch. They have a funnel-shaped mouth, which helps them to float and to obtain the tiny plants and animals they eat. After about three months the tadpoles have become miniature frogs and are ready to leave the water and hunt small insects.

The Asiatic horned frog's eyes have vertical pupils, like a cat's, which suggests that it is nocturnal.

43 red-eyed tree-frog

Agalychnis callidryas

Distribution: Central America
Habitat: low-lying tropical forest
Diet: insects

This frog has spectacular markings: its body is bright green, its eyes are red, its toes are orange-yellow and it has a patch of yellow with blue stripes down each side.

Red-eyed tree-frogs spend the daytime high up in the trees, coming down to the ground at dusk.

During the breeding season the males croak to attract females, who carry the males on their backs while they look for a suitable place to lay their eggs. These are laid on the undersides of leaves that overhang water. (The tips of

the red-eyed tree-frog's toes and fingers are flat, so it can cling to the
undersides of leaves.) The eggs need to be in a moist place so that they do
not dry out. A female red-eyed tree-frog can lay several clumps, each
containing between 25 and 80 eggs.

After about seven days the tadpoles wriggle out of the eggs and drop into
the water below. They feed on microscopic plants and animals filtered from
the water. After about 80 days they change into frogs and can move on to
land.

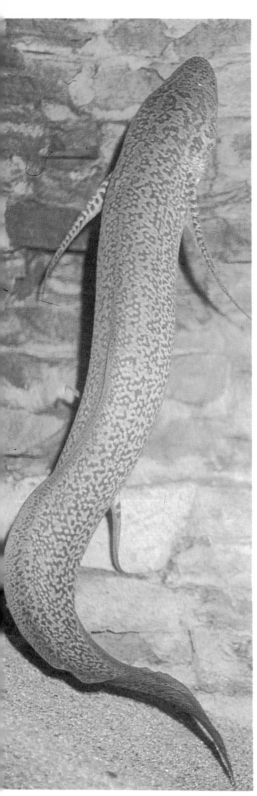

44 African lungfish

Protopterus annectans

Distribution: West Africa
Habitat: rivers and lakes that dry out from time to time
Diet: fish and amphibians (worms and freshwater shrimps when small)

The African lungfish is often called a living fossil, because it belongs to a family of fish that is over 400 million years old.

Unlike all other fish, the lungfish has a pair of lungs as well as gills and can breathe air.

If the river where it lives dries up in the summer, as often happens, the lungfish will bury itself in mud and surround itself with slime. This dries out to form a cocoon. The fish breathes through a tube to the outside, but does not feed. It gets the small amount of energy it needs from its muscles. The lungfish can survive for up to four years in the cocoon, wriggling out to take up its normal life again when rain falls.

Shortly after it emerges from its cocoon, the male persuades several females to lay their eggs in a nest of mud. He guards the eggs and the young, which at first look like tadpoles, with external gills. After about 50 days the young become more fish-like. They grow very quickly so that they are ready to survive the next drought.

45 red piranha

Serrasalmus nattereri

Distribution: Amazon Basin
Habitat: rivers and flood plains
Diet: fish, other small animals and seeds

Most people think that piranhas are ferocious fish that attack large animals, including people, and reduce them to bones within minutes, but there is no real evidence that this happens. Their main diet is fish.

There are many different species of piranha; the red piranha is one of the few that hunts in large shoals, numbering up to several thousand. These piranhas usually attack their prey from behind, ripping off large chunks of flesh.

Piranhas have particularly well-developed jaws with strong muscles. Their teeth are sharp and pointed and the upper teeth fit in between the lower teeth. There is some evidence to suggest that piranhas may even be cannibals and eat their own kind.

Very little is known about how piranhas breed in the wild. They probably spawn during January and February, when the rivers flood.

46 dragon fish

Pterois volitans

Distribution: Indian and Pacific Oceans (widespread)
Habitat: rocks and reefs
Diet: other fish and crabs, shrimps, etc.

The dragon fish has probably been given more names than any other fish, including "scorpion fish", "zebra fish" and "lion fish". Its beautiful stripy colouring helps to camouflage it on the reefs so that unsuspecting prey do not see it until it is too late. At breeding time, the dragon fish's colouring helps it to identify others of the same species.

As well as being one of the most attractive fishes in the world, the dragon fish is one of the most dangerous: it produces poison at the base of the spines of its dorsal fin. If threatened, a dragon fish will spread out its fins; any predator foolish enough to ignore this warning is likely to be spiked with poison. People can die from dragon-fish poison.

47 mudskipper

Periophthalmus sp.

Distribution: coastal regions of Africa and Asia
Habitat: mangrove swamps close to river deltas
Diet: insects and small shrimp-like crustaceans

Mudskippers probably spend more time out of water than in it. Their large, mobile eyes are set high on the head and can see very well in air. They have special fins that they use to drag themselves across the mud and can even climb trees! On land, they are protected by their tough, spongy skin.

Mudskippers, like most fish, do not have lungs, so breathing in air could be a problem. They overcome this by keeping their mouth closed and covering their gills with a large mouthful of water. They may absorb some oxygen through their skin.

Mudskippers often gather in groups of 20 or 30. The females lay their eggs in tunnel-shaped "nests" that the males build out of mud. To begin with, the young fish's eyes are on the side of the head and their fins are short. As they develop, their eyes move to the top of the head, their fins grow longer and they are ready to move out on to the mud.

48 red-kneed tarantula

Brachypelma smithi

Distribution: Mexico
Habitat: desert
Diet: insects

The red-kneed tarantula is well adapted to its desert habitat. It has a tough outer skeleton to cut down water loss and avoids the heat of the sun by being nocturnal. During the day it hides in rock crevices which it lines with silk.

Instead of spinning webs to catch prey, the red-kneed tarantula roams about in search of insects. It snatches the prey, then paralyses it with poison produced in a pair of pointed fangs near its mouth and injects the insect with digestive juices. This turns the insect's insides into a pulp that the spider sucks in through its mouth. The red-kneed tarantula's poison is not normally harmful to humans but a bite is said to feel like a bad wasp-sting.

The female tarantula lays her eggs in a cocoon of silken threads. The eggs hatch within a few weeks. The spiderlings, which look like miniature adults, moult between six and ten times before they are mature, at about three years old. When a tarantula moults, its outer skeleton splits around the side and the top lifts off like a cap. The spider's body emerges first and then it pulls its legs through. The new outer skeleton is soft at first so the spider must hide from predators for a while.

49 peacock butterfly

Inachis io

Distribution: temperate areas of Europe and Asia
Habitat: hedgerows and gardens
Diet: nectar from flowers (as adult) and nettle leaves (as caterpillar)

The peacock butterfly's four large, blue-and-yellow "eyes" are on the upper side of its wings. They are hidden when the butterfly is at rest and folds its wings above its back. The undersides of the wings are a mottled brown, which is good camouflage. If a predator comes too close, the peacock butterfly spreads open its wings. Seeing not just one pair, but two pairs of eyes frightens off the attacker.

Like all butterflies and moths, the peacock butterfly has a four-stage life cycle. The eggs are laid in the spring, on nettle plants. When the caterpillar emerges, it feeds on the young nettle leaves for six to eight weeks. Then, after eating its fill, it climbs into a bush, hangs from a branch and turns into a chrysalis (pupa). About two weeks later the adult butterfly emerges from the chrysalis.

Generally, the peacock butterfly has a short life, although some hibernate in sheltered places and emerge in the spring to begin the next generation.

50 greenfly

Aphis sp.

Distribution: temperate regions worldwide
Habitat: trees and other plants
Diet: sap (the juice of plants)

When a greenfly pierces a plant stem with its sharp, pointed mouth-tube the pressure inside the stem forces sap into its body. The greenfly does not use all the sugar in the sap: some passes out and is often taken by ants (this is why ants are said to "milk" greenfly).

Losing juice often weakens plants. Another problem is that greenfly can spread virus diseases, so farmers and gardeners regard them as pests.

In the spring, greenfly with wings fly to plants such as roses. All of them are females and they can give birth to hundreds of female young (but no males) without mating. These female offspring can have hundreds of female young of their own in the same way. All these greenfly are born live, not from eggs.

In the autumn a generation of males and females is produced. These usually have wings and fly to trees for the winter, where they mate. The mated females lay eggs that will hatch the following spring, when the whole process begins again.

Things to do

- There are extraordinary animals all around you – the greenfly is just one example – and there is a lot still to be discovered about such creatures, however common they seem. You could investigate animals in your own garden or backyard, starting with a particular species of bird, spider, fly, beetle, butterfly, snail, etc. Make notes and detailed drawings about it. What does it eat? Which animals eat it? How does it behave when threatened? Does it keep to a clearly defined territory? How does it reproduce?
- There are always unusual animals to see in zoos. When you visit a zoo, take photographs of the animals and make notes to keep in a project book. Zoo guidebooks and the labels on the enclosures usually supply useful information.
- Many countries issue postage stamps featuring animals. You could start a collection, grouping the stamps by their country of origin or by the types of animals (all the mammals could go together, for example). Display some of your stamps on a world map, drawing lines to link the stamps and the countries they come from.
- Paint or describe your own imaginary extraordinary animal. Try to make sure it could survive in the habitat you choose for it. Read books to help you decide which group it belongs to (mammal, bird, reptile, fish, insect, etc.), what it would eat and how it would move, breathe and reproduce.
- Try to imagine the reasons why some of the animals in this book developed in such strange ways.
- Choose an unusual animal to study, using books or visiting zoos or making field trips. If possible, compare it with a closely related animal. How are they similar? How do they differ?
- Look out for and watch wildlife programmes on television. They often show extraordinary animals and how they live.

Books to read

The Amateur Naturalist, Gerald and Lee Durrell. Hamish Hamilton.
Atlas of the Living World, F. Colombo. Burke.
Discovering Life on Earth, David Attenborough. Collins.
Encyclopedia of Reptiles, Amphibians and Other Cold-blooded Animals, Maurice Burton and Robert Burton. Octopus.
The Guinness Book of Animal Facts and Feats, Gerald L. Wood. Guinness.
Insect Life, T. Rowland-Entwistle and Oxford Scientific Films Limited. The World You Never See series, Hamlyn.
The Living World of Animals. Reader's Digest.
Mysteries and Marvels of Nature, R. Morris, B. Cork and K. Goaman. Usborne.
The Pond, G. Thompson, J. Coldrey and G. Bernard. Collins.

Glossary

adapt change to be better suited.

albino person or animal without usual colouring pigment in skin and hair (these are white). The eyes are usually pink.

alga (plural **algae**) simple, primitive plants, usually living in water. For example, some seaweeds are algae.

amphibian an animal, such as a frog, toad or newt, that is able to live both on land and in water.

camouflaged disguised by colouring or pattern in order to blend in with the background.

canine tooth sharp, pointed tooth found in mammals, sometimes called a fang.

carrion dead, rotting animal flesh.

casque in birds, a helmet-shaped growth on top of the head usually made of bone and covered with tough skin.

conifer cone-bearing tree, such as a pine or spruce.

crop milk liquid made in a bird's crop (part of its gullet) and fed to its young.

crustacean animal with a hard shell and jointed legs that usually lives in water, e.g. a crab, shrimp or lobster.

delta triangular area of sand (or mud, etc.) deposited near a river mouth, where the river divides into several branches.

distribution where a particular group of animals is normally found.

domesticated tame, or under human control.

dorsal of or on the back.

endangered species classed as endangered are those that appear to be in immediate danger of extinction.

gestation period the period of time it takes a young mammal to develop inside its mother.

habitat the natural home of a plant or animal.

hibernate spend the winter asleep or inactive.

incubate keep eggs warm (by sitting on them, perhaps) so that the young develop properly.

marsupial a mammal, e.g. a kangaroo, that rears its young in a pouch.

migrate move to a different area.

nocturnal active during the night.

pigment natural chemical that can cause the colouring of a plant or animal.

plankton floating or drifting plants or animals, usually microscopic (extremely small).

predator an animal that hunts, kills and feeds on other animals.

prehensile tail tail that can grasp.

prey an animal killed by other animals for food.

Primates the name given to the group of mammals that includes lemurs, monkeys, apes and man.

regurgitate bring up food from the stomach or crop.

rodent a mammal with strong front teeth for gnawing, e.g. rats, mice, squirrels and porcupines.

savannah a grassy plain with few trees, in tropical and subtropical regions.

scrub an area of stunted trees and low bushes.

solitary living alone.

species a group of animals or plants that can interbreed.

tundra flat, treeless areas in the Arctic.

vegetation plant life; the plants growing in a certain place.

vertebrate an animal that has a backbone (or spine). Fish, amphibians, reptiles, birds and mammals are vertebrates.